The Adventures of
MOLLY

Molly Moves to a New House

a furry tale by
Hilari Rogers
illustrated by Lydia Perez-Reyes

The Adventures of Molly: Molly Moves to a New House
Copyright © 2021 by Hilari Rogers

First Edition

Paperback ISBN: 978-1-68515-511-7
eBook ISBN: 978-1-68515-512-4

To our silly Molly
that brings us love and excitement
every day.

Molly is a dog.

She lives
in a big house
in the city.

Her Mom takes
her for walks
and she likes to
pick things up.

Sometimes Cooper comes to visit her.
They share bones
and play around the house.

One day Molly's Dad said they would move near a lake.

Molly was
a little worried
about moving.

A big moving truck
took them to the new house.

The new house has a big yard,
a fish pond, and is on a lake.

Molly and Cooper like the new friends at the house.

Many goldfish are in the pond

and a big white bird.

Molly and Cooper
like to play at the new house.

CPSIA information can be obtained
at www.ICGtesting.com
Printed in the USA
LVRC091243021121
702215LV00003B/88